16 dramas for all-age worship

Sketches for the Church Year

David Walker

First published in 2001 by
KEVIN MAYHEW LTD
Buxhall
Stowmarket IP14 3BW

9 8 7 6 5 4 3 2 1 0

ISBN 1 84003 768 7
Catalogue Number 1500442

Cover design by Jonathan Stroulger
Edited and typeset by Elisabeth Bates

Printed in Great Britain

Contents

Introduction

The following sketches are designed for use in normal parish worship, perhaps to replace the sermon slot, or for family worship, or for some special occasion. They are written for use at different times of the Church's year or to amplify a particular incident from the Bible.

The sketches are intended to be easy to use, requiring only a few actors, and little in the way of scenery, props, or costume. Dialogue and settings may be changed to suit local situations. Experience shows that, although the sketches can be performed with the actors reading their words, they work so much more effectively when the lines have been learned.

Drama is a very useful way of challenging people, making them think, and stressing a particular theme or point. Where this can be done with humour, so much the better, and it is hoped that at least some of the sketches will make people smile.

The sketches could also be used effectively outside of worship on other suitable occasions. These might include missions, street theatre, parish away-days, discussion groups, etc.

Each sketch is prefaced by what are intended to be helpful notes to assist the performance.

Baptism preparation

This sketch has been used as an introduction to a session of baptism preparation, although it could be used at any stage during the process. It tries to identify an area in which parents will have clear expectations for their children, and, from there, to lead them to reflect on their expectations about baptism. We tended to use the same person to play the Head and the Vicar, but two different actors might make the distinction better.

Following the sketch, the nature of baptism is explored further, and whether or not this is what the parents are looking for. The practical arrangements surrounding the baptism of their child is also dealt with.

The sketch can also be used very effectively as a teaching aid at a family service or at a baptism service. In my parochial experience, it is often the mother who takes the lead in religious matters and the father often seems to have been dragged along unwillingly. The sketch over-emphasises this relationship. The Dad has to be played very dead-pan and droll so that he can make the grand statement at the end. The family name and the street name can be changed to suit local situations.

The scene is the study of a headteacher in any school.
The Head is sitting at the desk and there is a knock at the door.

Head   Come in!

Enter Mum and Dad.

Head   Do come in. It's Mr and Mrs Smith, isn't it? Do have a seat. *(They sit down)* Now, what can I do for you?

Mum   We'd like to get our son's name down for this school, Headmaster. We want him to have a good education, a good start in life, and we think this is the best school for him – don't we, Dad?

Dad	Um . . . oh . . . yes . . .
Head	Quite, quite. You've made a very good choice. I'll just take a few details. *(He takes paper and pen)* What's your son's full name?
Mum	John Simon Smith.
Head	Address?
Mum	17 Margaret Thatcher Close.
Head	Any brothers or sisters?
Mum	Just one baby sister. She's only four months old. A little love, isn't she, Dad?
Dad	Um . . . oh . . . yes . . .
Head	Right, that's fine, and I'm sure you've made a very wise decision. Goodbye!
Mum	Um . . . excuse me . . . but . . . when does he start school?
Head	Sorry, I'm not with you.
Mum	When does John start school? When does he come for his lessons? When does he begin his education?
Head	Oh, I see. You needn't worry about that. He's got his name down, he's joined. That's all he needs.
Mum	But he'll never learn to read and write and count and everything just because his name's on the school roll – will he, Dad?
Dad	Um . . . oh . . . no . . .

Head   I see, you're going to be like those trendy parents who think once their child's name is down we have to put up with them for the next few years. Have them at school! Teach them things! I don't know what the world is coming to. It wasn't like this in the old days. I'm sorry, but we only take names at this school and we pass them on once they're old enough to start work.

Mum   Well, we're not registering him at this school! I've never heard anything so ridiculous! Come on, Dad. We're leaving!

Dad   Um . . . oh . . . right . . .

Exit Mum and Dad.

The actor who played the Head, or another actor, now fills the roll of the Vicar who is sitting at his desk in his study. There is a knock at the door.

Vicar   *(Gets up and goes to the door to let them in)* Hello, do come in.

Enter Mum and Dad.

Vicar   Please have a seat. *(They sit)* What can I do for you?

Mum   We'd like our little girl christened, Vicar; wouldn't we, Dad?

Dad   Um . . . oh . . . yes . . .

Vicar   Good. Sometimes you'll hear it called Baptism, but don't worry about that. Christening and Baptism are the same thing. Now, are you sure you know what Baptism is all about before you take this important step?

Mum   Oh yes. We do, don't we, Dad?

Dad   Um . . . oh . . . yes . . .

Mum	We shall come to church one Sunday and get her done. Get her name down on God's list. I always say they're not right till you've had them Christened. It's tradition, isn't it, Dad?
Dad	Um . . . oh . . . yes . . .
Vicar	But what about coming to church? Joining the Church Family and getting a Christian education for yourselves and for your baby?
Mum	Oh, you're not one of those trendy Vicars who expects us to come to church, are you? We just want to have her done, that's all – don't we, Dad?
Dad	Um . . . oh . . . yes . . .
Vicar	But, being baptised means starting a whole new life for yourselves and for your baby. It's more than just a ceremony for getting her name down and having her 'done'. After all, you would think it very strange if all a school did were to take children's names and then never wanted to see them again, wouldn't you?
Dad	I think he's got a point there, Mother. Perhaps we had better go away and think about it.
Mum	Um . . . oh . . . yes . . .

Exit Mum and Dad.

Be prepared

Written with the season of Advent in mind, this sketch asks us to question our whole notion of being prepared. In Advent we are to prepare, not only for the coming of Jesus at Christmas, but also for his Second Coming.

As Christians, we are always tempted to believe that we are the ones who are ready, whilst those outside are passing by at an incredible speed, unaware of what it is all really about.

During his ministry on earth, Jesus often mocked, spurned, chastised, and even ignored those who believed they were spiritually and religiously ready, turning instead to those considered unfit and unready.

In this sketch it is the one who appears to be more prepared, the one who has all the answers, who misses the train. Perhaps we need to take time out to look more closely at our own lives so we do not make the same mistake.

The Passenger and Scout are standing on a platform waiting for a train. The Passenger, dressed in ordinary clothes, carries a large suitcase. The Scout is in full uniform, with a rucksack and sleeping bag and various items tied to his belt.

Passenger   I hope the train isn't going to be late.

Scout   It doesn't matter if it is, I've got my flask and my sandwiches, I'm prepared. That's the Scouts' motto, you know, 'Be Prepared'.

Passenger   It's a bit draughty on this platform.

Scout   Never mind, I've got my scarf. _(Takes out scarf and wraps it round his neck)_

Passenger   My feet are killing me! Why aren't there any seats on this flipping station to sit on?

Scout	*(Takes out shooting stick and unfolds seat)* Always be prepared, that's my motto. *(He sits)*
Passenger	The train must be late now. I wish I had remembered to put my watch on. I can see it now, lying on the table at home.
Scout	That's no problem for a Scout. If you hold your arm up straight to the sun *(He puts his arm up in the air)* and you look at the angle you can tell it is now ten past two.
Passenger	But there isn't any sun in here. You can't possibly tell the time like that. You're just making it up.
Scout	No I'm not! If there was some sun I could tell the time easily, but anyway, it is ten past two.
Passenger	How do you know that then?
Scout	It says so, over there, on the station clock.
Passenger	Oh very droll. I would eat this orange *(Taking out orange)* if only I had remembered to bring a knife to peel it with.
Scout	No problem. Give it here. *(Takes orange and gets knife from his belt)* This super Scout knife can perform a multitude of tasks. Peeling an orange is no problem. *(Begins to peel orange)* Do you know, there is even a thing for taking a stone out of a horse's hoof?
Passenger	Do you come across many horses with stones in their hooves, then?
Scout	No, but I meet a lot of unprepared people who need their oranges peeled.
Passenger	What if the train is cancelled? It's the only one today you know. We'll have to spend the night here on this platform. They don't even have a waiting room here. It's going to be very cold and uncomfortable.

Scout	Not for a Scout, it's not. I've got my sleeping bag. You see, we're always prepared for everything.
Passenger	My case is so heavy, it will be all I can do to lift it onto the train. How do you manage to carry so much?
Scout	You just have to be prepared. A good rucksack is essential, and we learn all kinds of knots so I can carry everything I need. Do you know, we have a knot for every occasion?
Passenger	Wow! That is impressive! I think perhaps I would have been wise to have been a Scout.
Scout	Absolutely! They teach us everything and, what's more, we are prepared for every situation. Nothing can ever faze a Scout.
Passenger	Here comes the train.
	Three or four people enter each behind the other. They use their arms like pistons and make a train sound.
Passenger	*(Reaches into his pocket)* Must check I've got my ticket. I'm always afraid I'll forget it. No, here it is. *(Shows ticket)*
	The train stops and Passenger gets on behind the others. They begin to move away slowly, using their arms as pistons and making a train noise.
Scout	Ticket! Oh no, I forgot to get a ticket!
Passenger	*(As train leaves)* Bye! Isn't it good to be prepared?
	Exit train.
Scout	Missed it again! Oh well, I guess I'll have to be prepared . . . to walk.
	Exit Scout.

Busy! Busy!

The story of Mary and Martha and the visit of Jesus to their home is very familiar to us. We all know that Mary is praised for choosing to listen and learn at the feet of Jesus whilst Martha is gently chastened for being distracted by the everyday tasks of running a home. We hear the reading in church and most of us probably applaud Mary for her decision and can see the folly of Martha and all her worries.

But in our everyday lives, most of us spend more of our time being a Martha than we do being a Mary. Our days are spent agonising over and wrestling with all the pressures of daily living. It is generally the practicalities of life that take up the hours, rather than the pursuit of ultimate truth and meaning.

In this sketch we see Mary being praised by Jesus for choosing as she has, but because I believe Jesus also had a great understanding and concern for the practicalities of life, we see him giving Martha his support too, whilst still pointing her to a better way. I realise this last bit is not contained in the biblical account, but to me it doesn't seem too unlikely, or out of character for Jesus, and does find accord in the overall message of the Gospel.

The scene is the home of Mary and Martha. It can be played either in traditional costume and furniture or in modern dress with modern furniture. A chair and low table are centre stage. Martha is a busy character who is always bustling about.

Enter Mary. She sits on the chair with her feet on the table and begins to read a book.

Enter Martha.

Martha   Busy, busy, always busy! So much to do, so little time to do it in. *(Looks at Mary)* If only I had some help.

(Mary looks up, shakes her head, sighs, and returns to her book)

Martha	He'll be here soon, you know, Mary.
Mary	I know, Martha.
Martha	We will never be ready.
Mary	I'm ready now.
Martha	Just look at the place! We can't let him come here with it looking like this. It needs a good clean up. I'll get a duster.

Exit Martha – she returns with a feather duster and begins dusting. She goes to dust the table.

Martha	Feet!
Mary	Pardon?
Martha	Move your feet, I'm dusting!

Mary moves her feet, but puts them back on the table as soon as Martha has finished.

Martha	I suppose it's too much to ask you to do a bit of baking? They'll be hungry when they arrive, I expect.
Mary	Definitely!
Martha	What? They'll definitely be hungry, or it's definitely too much to ask?
Mary	Both!
Martha	What are you reading anyway? It can't be that important.
Mary	The collected teachings of Jesus. I'm revising before he gets here.

Martha	Look, he's coming here for a rest. Don't you go bothering him with all your daft questions. Try to remember you're a woman. I know it's difficult for you, but women do the housework, raise the kids, and ask their husbands in the privacy of their own home if they want to know about deep religious truths.
Mary	I haven't got a husband.
Martha	No, more's the pity! If you had he would stop you having all these fanciful notions and you might have learned how to do a bit of housework as well.
Mary	Stop panicking and don't be so conventional! Jesus won't care whether it's tidy or not. He's more interested in our inner state than what appears on the outside; it says so here on page 36.
Martha	That's all very well, but a wonderful inner state isn't much use if you've nothing to eat and drink and nowhere clean to sit down.
Mary	I'll help when I've finished my book, if there's time.
Martha	Don't put yourself out! Why should today be any different? Just because we have the Master coming is no reason to expect I might get some help for once! You sit there and fill your head full of nonsense; I'll take care of everything. I'll finish the cleaning, do the washing, and then in my spare time, I'll prepare a meal for when they arrive. Inner state indeed!
	Exit Martha.
Mary	*(Looks up from her book)* She'll wear herself out that one. Old before her time, you mark my words.
	There is a knock at the door. Mary stands.

Enter Martha with Jesus and three or four followers.

Mary shows Jesus to the chair, then she and his followers sit at his feet. Jesus does the actions of teaching them, but silently. They nod and respond appropriately.

Martha   Jesus, you and your friends are welcome to our home. I hope everything is to your satisfaction. I do apologise for the mess, but *(Looks at Mary)* I've had no help, you see.

Everyone is ignoring her. Jesus continues to teach, the others listen.

Martha   *(Feeling her arm)* Whoops! Have I become invisible again?

Everyone continues to ignore her.

Martha   Don't worry that I slaved all day and worked my fingers to the bone for your visit! You just carry on as if I'm not here.

Everyone continues to ignore her.

Martha   Oh, you *are* doing. Right! Fine! I'll just go back to the kitchen then.

Everyone continues to ignore her.

Martha   Yes, that's what I'll do. I'll put the kettle on, shall I?

Everyone continues to ignore her.

Martha   Does anyone take sugar?

Everyone continues to ignore her.

Martha   I'll take that as a 'No'.

Everyone continues to ignore her.

Martha   Right, I'm going then. I'll be back in a minute. Will you be all right without me?

Everyone continues to ignore her.

Martha   Right.

Exit Martha.

Jesus continues to teach silently, as the others listen.

Enter Martha (she taps Jesus on the shoulder).

Martha   Look, I know all this is jolly important and everything, but don't you care that I'm doing all the work while Mary sits here doing nothing? I mean, you won't be so happy when you haven't got any supper, will you?

Jesus   Martha, Martha, don't make such a fuss. Mary has chosen to sit here and learn about salvation, eternal life, and my Father's kingdom. This is far more important than cooking and cleaning.

Martha   What, even for a woman?

Jesus   Yes, Martha, even for a woman. *(He stands and puts his arm round Martha)* Come on, we're finished for now, we'll all come and help you with the supper.

Exit All.

The chefs

In Luke's Gospel (14:28-32) Jesus urges his hearers to assess very carefully the cost of being a disciple before making such a momentous decision. It is only by doing this that we can ever hope to finish the journey upon which we have embarked.

Using the formula of the popular television programme, *Ready, Steady, Cook!* this sketch shows in a humorous way what happens if we are too ambitious, without paying any attention to the reality of what is before us. It also reminds us that good intentions are not enough unless they are backed up by what is realistic and achievable and by a determination to see things through to the end.

There are two tables at the front, one each side. Behind one, towards the back, is a large sign with a 'Cross' on it and behind the other a large sign with a '£' symbol on it. On each table is a mixing bowl, a wooden spoon, some ingredients, which do not need to be real, and a recipe book. Behind each table is an oven. This can simply be a box with 'oven' written on it that opens at the front. In Ivor's oven (the 'Cross') there needs to be a sponge cake ready. On coming into church the congregation need to be given a piece of card with the two symbols, 'Cross' and '£', one on each side.

The names of the Chefs can be changed to suit the situation, but then some of the dialogue will need changing.

Enter Presenter.

Presenter   Good morning, ladies and gentlemen, and welcome to today's edition of *Get Set, Cook!*, your favourite cookery programme where we ask, 'What's cooking in your life?' First, let's meet today's celebrity chefs, starting with the man who put the cream into 'custard creams', your friend and mine, Mr Ivor Biscuit!

Enter Ivor.

Presenter   Welcome! Are you really ready for this today?

Ivor   Like a jelly.

Presenter   How's that?

Ivor   A bit wobbly, but dead set and hoping to be a big winner at the party.

Ivor stands behind table with 'Cross' symbol.

Presenter   And now let's meet your opponent for today. He's a regular favourite of ours. The man who gave us 'upside down pudding' when he dropped it on the floor, the one and only, Paulie Gateau!

Enter Paulie.

Presenter   Welcome to you too! You know Ivor?

Paulie nods and shakes hands with Ivor.

Presenter   Are you fully prepared for battle?

Paulie   Like an undercooked chicken!

Presenter   Really?

Paulie   Meaty, tasty, juicy and a little bit dangerous.

Paulie stands behind table with '£' sign.

Presenter   *(Goes to Ivor)* What have you decided to cook for us today?

Ivor   Given the ingredients, butter, flour, eggs, sugar, cocoa, and cooking chocolate, I thought I would make a sponge cake with chocolate butter icing and chocolate topping.

Presenter   Sounds very tasty! Not so good for the old diet, but that can always start tomorrow. I know mine always does.

Presenter goes to Paulie.

Presenter   Paulie, you've been given the same ingredients, so what have you chosen to make for us?

Paulie   I think I can make something better than that very modest offering over there. I shall make a very rich Christmas cake and, if there's time, I'll do a little decoration to go with it.

Presenter   Isn't it a bit early to be making Christmas cake?

Paulie   Not at all! If you make it now, it gives you lots of time to feed it with brandy, then, come Christmas, you have a lovely moist, rich cake.

Presenter   *(Comes to centre)* OK, you have as long as it takes after I say the magic words, 'Get set, cook!'

Presenter   *(Goes to Ivor)* So what are you doing first?

Ivor   First we cream the butter and sugar together until soft, light and fluffy.

Paulie   *(Reads from recipe book)* 'Sieve together dry ingredients. Chop cherries and almonds'. *(Looks through ingredients)* Cherries? Almonds? Whoops! Back in a minute.

Exit Paulie.

Ivor   Now we beat in the eggs a little at a time.

Enter Paulie.

Paulie   No cherries or almonds. Oh well, we'll just manage without them.

Presenter   *(Goes to Paulie)* And how are we doing over here?

Paulie   Great! *(Reads from book)* 'Cream butter and sugar' *(Starts to do that)* 'and stir in black treacle.' *(Looks through ingredients)* Won't be a tick!

Exit Paulie.

Presenter   He seems very busy! *(Goes to Ivor)* What are we doing now?

Ivor   You seem to be presenting a cookery programme, and I am about to fold in the flour *(He does this)*.

Enter Paulie.

Paulie   No black treacle. I don't suppose it's that important. We'll manage without it.

Presenter   *(Goes to Paulie)* How is it going this side?

Paulie   Fantastic! *(Reads from book)* 'Gradually add beaten eggs to butter and sugar.' *(He does this, then continues to read)* 'Melt chocolate, cool and fold into mixture with flour, fruit and brandy.' *(Looks through ingredients)* Fruit? Brandy? I must have left them outside. I won't be long!

Exit Paulie.

Presenter   *(Goes to Ivor)* He's gone again! What's happening now?

Ivor   I'm putting the mixture into these two sponge tins and popping them in the oven. *(He does this)*

Enter Paulie.

Presenter *(Goes to Paulie)* Is everything all right?

Paulie Couldn't be better! No fruit or brandy, but they're not really important.

Presenter Really? But that's what makes a Christmas cake a Christmas cake, isn't it?

Paulie Only in a conventional sense. This is more your surreal Christmas cake. It needs to be eaten with the taste of the imagination. *(As he is saying this he puts the mixture in a tin and puts it in the oven)*

Presenter *(Goes to Ivor)* Is it ready yet?

Ivor Just about; I've made the butter cream and melted the chocolate while I've been waiting. *(Goes to oven and takes out perfect cake)* There we are, and if I had time I would fill it with my butter cream and coat the top with chocolate.

Presenter That looks truly wonderful! *(Goes to Paulie)* And how about this side?

Paulie *(Goes to oven and removes tin. It is just an uncooked mess)* Whoops! Forgot to turn on the oven. Never mind, I'm sure it will taste very nice. Do you want to try some?

Presenter I'll give it a miss if you don't mind. It looks rather 'poorly', if you'll forgive the pun. *(Comes to centre and talks to audience)* As always, it's up to you to choose the winner. Remember, you're voting on who made the most of the ingredients they were given. So, vote now, Crosses or Quids?

Audience hold up their cards.

Presenter It's close, well, no it's not really, the clear winner is Ivor!

Presenter *(Goes to Ivor)* Well done you! You win our special award for seeing the situation as it truly is.

Presenter *(Goes to Paulie)* Bad luck, you tried hard. Where do you think you went wrong?

Paulie I might have been just a touch over-ambitious given the ingredients I had.

Presenter A touch? You didn't really look at what was involved at all, did you?

Paulie Not really, but my intentions were good.

Presenter Never mind, at least there is one consolation.

Paulie What's that?

Presenter It was only cooking, it could have been real life. Come on, let's all go and enjoy Ivor's cake.

Exit All.

Christmas

Christmas is an ideal time for a sketch to be used in worship. During the Christmas period, the demand for services from church groups, secular groups, schools, etc., is often overwhelming. These are in addition to the many extra services we arrange as part of our own Christmas celebrations. Any additional material we can find is always welcome. Unfortunately, much of the dramatic material available is either a nativity play or a derivative of a nativity play.

This sketch seeks to take a different look at Christmas, rather than simply retelling the story.

We are well used to believing, and with some justification, that for most people Christmas is simply a commercial festival with little or no religious content. Like the lady behind me in the supermarket queue (and I swear this is true) who turned to her friend and said, 'It's disgusting, even the churches are trying to take over Christmas now!'

But we are less good at looking inwards at our own preoccupations and examining their relevance and meaning for today. Just as the world can so easily be too worldly, so can the Church be too churchy.

This sketch seeks to question both aspects, and to bring us back to the biblical reality of a God who is magisterial and omnipotent, as well as being present and incarnate. Flowing through all these many perceptions of God is his all-loving nature. For at its heart, this is the true message of Christmas.

Knowledge stands on stage, holding a large book, or next to a lectern with a book on it. Two adults stand stage left holding a processional cross. Skint stands centre stage.

Enter Pilgrim.

Pilgrim   I'm Pilgrim. *(To Knowledge)* Who are you?

Knowledge   I'm Knowledge. I know everything . . . well . . . nearly everything.

Pilgrim What is the good of that?

Knowledge Knowing things gives you power over other people. I'm going to hold up this card to them *(Points to audience)* to prove I know exactly what you will say next. *(Holds up card with WHAT written on it)*

Pilgrim What?

Knowledge *(Shows Pilgrim card)* See.

Pilgrim That is amazing! Perhaps you can help me; I'm looking for God.

Knowledge What do you want to find God for?

Pilgrim Because I'm told he has even more answers than you do.

Knowledge I doubt it. But if you want to find God, you must climb up to him, because he lives far above the sky in his beautiful heaven. *(Points)* Up that way.

Pilgrim How do I get up there?

Knowledge You make your way very slowly, by being good, reading a lot, praying a lot, and generally looking holy.

Pilgrim How do I look holy?

Knowledge Like this. *(He puts his hands together and looks up in a pious way. Pilgrim copies him)*

Enter Seeker.

Seeker Hello, I'm Seeker. What are you two doing?

Pilgrim We're looking holy.

Seeker   More like senile, if you ask me.

Knowledge   What would you know? I'm Knowledge, I know everything.

Seeker   If you're so smart, perhaps you can help me. I'm Seeker and I'm looking for the Way.

Knowledge   What way?

Seeker   I don't know! If I knew that I wouldn't have to find it, would I?

Pilgrim   I must be off. Lots of spiritual climbing to do. *(He moves slowly, looking holy, towards something he can climb up, e.g. pulpit or stepladder)*

Seeker   So, what about this 'Way', then?

Knowledge   Do I have to do everything round here? Find a lively church and join it.

Seeker   OK. *(He moves to stage left where the two adults are standing with the cross)*

Pilgrim climbs part way up pulpit or ladder.

Knowledge   *(Shouts to Pilgrim)* How are you doing?

Pilgrim   *(Looking pious)* Very well! I've read two books, said lots of prayers and been on a course about healing. I'm getting much closer now.

Knowledge   *(Shouts to Seeker)* How about you?

Seeker   *(With arms up in the air)* Wonderful! We sing lots of happy songs, hold prayer meetings and have a really super time. I think I'm finding it.

Enter Pauper (dressed as a tramp).

Pauper   *(Goes to Seeker)* Spare a coin or two for a poor pauper at Christmas.

Seeker   Come in! Come in! Join our Group! We'll pray for you.

Pauper   But I only want a few quid to see me over Christmas.

Seeker   You will be much better off in here with us. We will help you find the 'Way', once we have cleaned you up a bit.

Pauper   *(Goes to Pilgrim)* Spare a coin or two for a poor fellow at Christmas.

Pilgrim   Sorry, but I'm on my way to God. I haven't got time for anything else. Stop distracting me, I'm looking holy.

Pauper   More like senile . . . *(Goes to Knowledge)* Spare a coin or two for a poor fellow at Christmas.

Knowledge I'm Knowledge, I know everything.

Pauper   If you know everything, how do I get some money?

Knowledge Easy, get a job.

Pauper   But there are no jobs. What do I do now?

Knowledge There are some very good government schemes. Try one of those.

Pauper   Will that get me a job?

Knowledge Probably not, but it will give you something to do for a few weeks. There is another fellow over there waiting for the same thing.

Pauper goes to join Skint.

Pauper   Hello there. Who are you?

Skint   I'm Skint, and before you ask, that is my name. Skint by name and skint by nature.

They shake hands.

Knowledge   *(Shouts to Pilgrim who has climbed higher)* How are you doing?

Pilgrim   Not bad, but I still haven't found him. I thought I was getting nearer, but he seems to have disappeared again.

Skint   Open those hands if you want to see God.

Pilgrim   What?

Skint   Open your hands. What do you see?

Pilgrim   *(Opens hands and looks at them)* I see the marks of the nails.

Skint   Then that is where you will find God. Come down. You will never reach him up there.

Pilgrim comes down and joins Skint.

Knowledge   *(Shouts to Seeker)* Have you found the 'Way' yet?

Seeker   No, we still have a lovely time, but we seem to be stuck where we are.

Skint   Open your doors if you want to see God.

Seeker   *(Opens pretend doors)* I can't see him.

Skint Look closely. You will see him in all those people passing by.

Seeker and few members of audience join Skint.

Knowledge *(To audience)* That's all the thanks I get! *(To characters on stage)* Don't ask me for help again, if you're going to ignore my advice. I don't know why I bother.

Skint Get your eyes out of that book and look around you. Knowledge isn't only in words. It's in all you see, the people you meet, the kindness and the love you give and receive.

Knowledge looks up and looks around and then joins Skint.

Pauper Who are you really?

Skint Who, me? No one important, only God.

Exit All.

The C.O.S.I. Club

In Acts 11:1-18, we read of Peter's vision at Joppa where he is commanded not to call unclean anything God has declared to be clean. The vision is linked to one of the first great disputes to hit the Church. In essence it was about whether those who wanted to be Christians had to first become Jews, or whether they could simply be followers of Christ as they were. It's perhaps hard for us to imagine what a great leap it was for Jewish Christians to accept Gentiles as their equals without any of the rigours of the Jewish religion being applied to them, but that is what happened.

Today we may be tempted to believe that this entire dispute is a long way behind us and was long ago resolved, but I suspect it is still with us, only in a different guise. Is there not still a temptation within congregations to expect everyone to conform to a norm and a type, which is 'like we are' before they can truly be accepted in?

This sketch simply takes that phenomenon to the extreme to show how it can still exist and operate within the Church today.

The C.O.S.I. Club is pronounced Cosy Club.

There is a big sign at the front saying:
The C.O.S.I. Club
All New Members
Welcome

Three committee members sit behind a desk; there is a chair the other side.

Enter Harvey (who wants to be a member and is appearing before the committee).

Member 1 Hello, do come in. Have a seat.

Harvey sits.

Member 2 Just relax, we three members only have to ask you a few questions.

Member 3 It's only a formality, everyone is welcome at the C.O.S.I. Club.

Member 1 Absolutely! Now then, can we have your full name?

Harvey Harvey, Oliver, Peter, Samuels.

Member 2 Oh dear, what a pity.

Harvey What's wrong?

Member 3 It's your initials, you see.

Harvey No, I don't see, I don't see at all.

Member 1 Your initials, they spell HOPS.

Harvey What's wrong with that?

Member 2 It gives the wrong impression. Makes us sound like a drinking club. Here at the C.O.S.I. Club we have our reputation to consider.

Member 3 Not to worry though, we'll change your name round. We'll register you as Peter, Oliver, Samuel, Harvey.

Member 1 *(Writes)* Oh yes, that's much better – POSH – I like the sound of that. Much more in keeping with the C.O.S.I. Club image.

Harvey But . . .

Member 2 Don't worry about it, it's only a technical matter, everyone is welcome here.

Member 3 Occupation?

Harvey Bus driver.

Member 1 *(Writes)* Public transport executive with special responsibility for consumer progression.

Member 3 Married?

Harvey Divorced.

Member 1 *(Writes)* Nuptially united, but socially separated.

Harvey Pardon?

Member 2 Don't worry, it's just a legal term we use. Any criminal convictions?

Harvey No! . . . Oh, I did get a speeding fine once.

Member 1 *(Writes)* Contributor to governmental road refunding scheme.

Member 3 Any pets?

Harvey Is this relevant?

Member 2 Oh yes, we're very pro-animal in the C.O.S.I. Club.

Member 1 Personally, I never eat anything else. *(He laughs at his joke)*

Harvey I have a dog.

Member 1 *(Writes)* Very good. That is always a plus point here.

Member 3 Favourite food?

Harvey Steak and kidney pie.

Member 1   (*Writes*) Boeuf et kidney en croûte.

Member 2   (*Stands, goes to Harvey and shakes his hand*) Welcome to the C.O.S.I. Club.

Harvey   (*Stands*) Thank you very much.

Member 3   (*Shakes Harvey's hand*) Fit in well here, you will. You're just like us.

Member 1   I've just remembered, there is one more question.

They all return to their seats.

Member 1   What is your postcode?

Harvey   NO1 2BE

Member 2   Oh dear, that will never do.

Harvey   What's wrong?

Member 3   Your postcode, that's what's wrong. NO1 2BE says No One To Be. You can't come in here with a postcode like that.

Member 1   I don't suppose you would consider moving house?

Harvey   Don't be ridiculous!

Member 2   It's either that, or no membership of the C.O.S.I. Club.

Harvey   I've never heard anything so ridiculous! Anyway, what does C.O.S.I. stand for?

Member 1   The Church of Saved Individuals.

Harvey Well, this is one individual who has just been saved . . . from making a big mistake. Goodbye!

Exit Harvey.

Member 3 Couldn't we just let him in anyway? He could sit at the back, out of the way.

Member 1 Don't be stupid, that's where we all sit.

Member 3 Oh yes, so it is. Silly me.

Exit Members 1, 2, and 3.

Dying for Easter

Easter, with its message of suffering and death in order that salvation might be restored to humanity, is a challenge both to the world and to the Church. Conventional wisdom does not sit easily with such precepts. We live in a society that believes in retaliation, the justifiable use of force, and that corporal punishment is the ultimate weapon in the correction of behaviour. These are views that find as wide a credence in church congregations as they do anywhere else.

And yet, these views surely have to find some challenge from the message of Easter. If Jesus proclaimed a message of love that was superior to all other powers, and lived out that message in the practicalities of his daily life, must it not challenge those of us who claim to be his followers to do the same?

But none of this seems easy or straightforward when we look at the world around us. This sketch seeks to highlight these issues and, in a light-hearted way, to show the dichotomy between the Gospel message and the normally accepted wisdom of the age.

Enter George.

George   (*To audience*) I'm right fed up! All I ever seem to do is work, work, work! More hours, greater efficiency, fewer staff, increased workload! Can't afford to give you a wage rise this year. Profits are down, costs are up, and the high rate of the pound is hitting exports. On and on and on, excuses, reasons, but it's always the workers who pay in the end.

Enter Bill.

Bill   Hi ya, George! How's tricks?

George   I'm fed up, Bill! All this working, it's getting me down. I mean, what's it all for? Where does it get us in the end?

Bill	Cheer up, at least you've got a job. There are plenty more who would be happy to take yours if you don't want it.
George	That's the trouble, that's why they get away with it all the time.
Bill	Get away with what?
George	Fleecing us! Paying us peanuts while they make their profits and live in style.
Bill	Cheer up, you old misery! You've got the summer to look forward to. A fortnight in Benidorm, isn't it?
George	Oh great! Two weeks drinking warm beer, the kids complaining they're bored, the missus telling me what a nice body the waiter has and how Spanish men are much more considerate than we are, and evenings spent listening to some drunken bloke from West Hartlepool singing 'Una Paloma Blanca!' What have I got to complain about? I only work all year for that!
Bill	Oh dear, you have got it bad. Never mind, Easter is coming; at least you'll get a day off.
George	Wonderful! Do you think there is anything in this Easter lark?
Bill	I dunno. Our Mary says there is. She's gone all religious, you know; prays, reads her Bible, goes to church! The other three are OK, they're still quite normal. I don't know where we went wrong with Mary.
George	I expect she'll grow out of it; they usually do.
Bill	She came in yesterday and said, 'I've got an Easter egg for the Vicar.' I said, 'That sounds like a fair swap.' I don't think she was very amused though.

George	I don't understand it anyway. What's the point of getting yourself killed? I mean, it can't do you any good, can it?
Bill	Mary says you have to be prepared to die in order to be born again, whatever that means. She says that we have to be prepared to suffer, if necessary, for the truth.
George	It makes no sense to me. I'm all for a bit of retaliation; you know, 'An eye for an eye and a tooth for a tooth', that's my motto.
Bill	I couldn't agree more, George. There are far too many of these 'do-gooders' about nowadays. Look out, here comes one now.
	Enter Vicar.
Vicar	*(To Bill)* Hello, you're Mary's dad, aren't you?
Bill	That's right, Vicar, and this is my mate George.
Vicar	*(Shakes hands)* How do you do. She's a lovely girl, Mary, such an enquiring mind, you must be very proud of her.
Bill	Absolutely, Vicar! I was just telling George here how pleased I am about Mary going to church and all, wasn't I, George?
George	*(Coughs)* Um . . . er . . .
Bill	Precisely!
Vicar	Perhaps we might see you in church this Easter.
Bill	I don't think so, Vicar. We were just saying, we're not much on this suffering lark. Seems a bit stupid getting yourself killed. Not much of a future in that, is there?

George   It's life you see, Vicar. It will get you nowhere if you let people walk all over you. I'm all for giving as good as I get. Get your retaliation in first – that's my motto.

Bill   I agree! We were just saying the problem with the country today is, people have gone soft. Youngsters have got no respect. They want a good clip round the ears, if you ask me. Too many 'do-gooders', that's the problem.

Vicar   In my experience there are only three kinds of people: 'do-gooders' of which there are few; 'do-badders' who seem equally scarce in number; and 'do-nothings' who appear to be in abundance.

George   Very clever! Give them a good thrashing, I say; that will teach them not to be violent.

Vicar   But, don't you see? Jesus was prepared to suffer, even to die, to show there is no greater power than love. Without his death Jesus couldn't have been raised and without his resurrection we couldn't have been set right with God.

Bill   Still sounds confusing to me. Dying in order to live. What kind of sense does that make? It would be a poor world if we all went round doing that kind of thing, and no mistake.

Vicar   Look, come to church with Mary and find out more. At least come at Easter, it can't do you any harm, can it?

Bill   I suppose not, but I can tell you now, you're not going to change my mind.

Vicar   I won't have to, we can leave God to do that.

Bill   I don't fancy his chances.

George   I'll say one thing for Easter though, Bill.

Bill   What's that?

George   At least we get an extra day off work.

Bill   And very welcome it is too.

George   After the way I've been feeling lately, I'm simply dying for Easter.

Vicar   I think you'll find that's been done already.

              Exit All.

The greatest show on earth

It is a common human trait to make ourselves feel better by finding someone who is demonstrably worse than us. We say, 'I know I'm not perfect, but I'm not as bad as so and so.' It's easy to say, 'I'm not a drug addict, a thief, a murderer, etc.', and in so doing take the light away from what we actually are.

This can be very true of Christians and church congregations. It is not by accident that many people outside the church believe that those inside think they are better than everyone else is. We have been less prominent in portraying church-going as the activity of the penitent sinner, the one who is unworthy, than we have of portraying it as the activity of the respectable.

Jesus told the parable of the Pharisee and the tax collector going to the temple to pray to show what our attitude towards others and ourselves should be, and what is and is not acceptable to God.

This sketch takes up that theme and contrasts the lives of two very different people. It calls us to question how we judge others and what the important qualities are we look for when we assess their worth. If we do this questioning honestly, most of us find that we assess others by using all the wrong qualities.

Two signs are on opposite sides at the front. The large sign says, 'The Greatest Show on Earth'; the other, much smaller, says, 'Who on Earth?'

Dud has no words but holds up signs that he shows to everyone. The Crowd look at Dud but then ignore him.

Good plays his part like a showman attracting the crowds. He is dressed in bright colourful clothes; Dud is dressed in dark drab clothes.

Enter Good and Dud.

(Good goes to the large sign, Dud to the small sign.)

Good   Roll up! Roll up! Come and see the greatest show on earth! The life and times of Ritchie Good! Rich by name and rich by nature; good by name and good by nature! Roll up! Roll up!

Enter Crowd (3 or 4 people would be sufficient). They all gather round Good.

(Dud holds up sign which says, 'I am Dud Sole; Dud by name and Dud by nature.' Crowd look briefly then turn back to Good)

Good   Get your tickets for the most fascinating journey through life! Born into a good family . . . Well, I would be with a name like that, wouldn't I?

(Dud holds up sign which says, 'Father in jail for thieving')

Good   Educated at Public School. I certainly learned my p's and q's.

(Dud holds up sign which says, 'Ate my peas and joined the dole queues')

Good   Left school with five A levels and went to university.

(Dud holds up sign which says, 'A-level Truancy')

Good   Joined father in the family business.

(Dud holds up sign which says, 'Joined father in family business')

Good   Business prospered!

(Dud holds up sign which says, 'Business Prospered')

Good   See me now for what I am – a pillar of society. Respectable and respected – I became a magistrate!

(The Crowd applaud and cheer)

(Dud holds up sign which says, 'Met a magistrate')

Good   Bought a large house with lots of rooms.

(Dud holds up sign which says, 'Got Room in Large House – HMP')

Good   Take your places for the next ride! See me as I join the local church. Soon at the top – made a large contribution to the roof appeal – led to me becoming churchwarden.

(Dud holds up sign which says, 'Top of church – lead withdrawal')

Good   Time to move on and move up! Bought an even bigger house with even more rooms!

(Dud holds up sign which says, 'Got room in Bigger House – HMP')

Good   Looked around, thought, hey, time to relax. So I sold the business and made a fortune! Now I enjoy myself driving in my brand-new Mercedes.

(Dud holds up sign which says, 'So will I, if he leaves it unlocked')

Good   It's been a good life all in all. I can't complain.

(Dud holds up sign which says, 'Me neither')

Good   But remember folks – I worked hard for it. I made it what it is! I put in all the effort! I have nothing I don't deserve!

(Dud holds up sign which says, 'Me neither')

Good   Hope you all enjoyed the show, the greatest show on earth! And now as I go to meet my Maker I can approach him with confidence. I can look him in the eye and say, 'God, I made the most of it down there. I did my bit; I was respectable and respected. I went to church, said my prayers, and even occasionally listened to the sermons. I was a pillar of society

(Dud holds up sign which says, 'Meet my Maker? Help!!!!')

Good   *(Waves goodbye)* That's it folks! Bye!

Crowd   *(Wave goodbye)* Bye Ritchie!

Exit Good.

(Dud holds up sign which says, 'Oh Dear! Can I go straight to Hell?')

Exit Dud.

Crowd 1   Who was that?

Crowd 2   Nobody important. The world is probably better off without him. A bit of a 'no good', if you ask me. Not someone to take any notice of. He was always doing harm to someone.

Crowd 1   That's one thing you could never say about Ritchie Good. He never did any harm to anyone.

Crowd 2   Makes you wonder though, did he ever do anyone any good?

Crowd 1   Search me! I guess that's something only God knows.

Crowd 2   I guess so.

Exit Crowd.

Heaven

Although based loosely on the parable of the rich man and Lazarus, this sketch can be used on any occasion where the themes of heaven and hell, judgement, etc., need to be explored.

The subjects of heaven, hell and judgement always give rise to heated debate. There are those who seem very sure of who is bound for heaven and who is bound for hell, but I have never been able to have that kind of certainty myself. If the Bible teaches us anything, it is surely that we are in no position to judge these matters for ourselves, let alone for others. When we look at the types of people Jesus called to him in his earthly life and those he was castigated for hanging around with, it seems to me heaven may well be full of those we least expected to be there.

Whatever the reality of heaven is, the sketch offers at least one plausible picture of how it might be. What does seem certain to me is that however it is, like Ivor in the sketch we will all have a lot to learn and many changes to undergo before we will feel fully at home there.

There is a sign which says 'Knock three times and ask for Peter'. There is also a broom.

Enter Ivor.

Ivor (*Knocks three times, nothing happens*) Come on! Come on! Hurry up! Time is money. (*He knocks again rapidly*)

Enter Peter (carrying a clipboard).

Peter All right! All right! Keep your halo on! (*Looks at Ivor*) Oh, it's you, Ivor, you haven't got one.

Ivor About time! Some of us have work to do. We haven't got all day, you know.

Peter	Actually, you have. In fact, you've got all eternity. Endless days, as it were.
Ivor	Talk sense, man! I only want a few directions. I seem to have lost my way.
Peter	You can say that again.
Ivor	Are you going to give me directions, or not?
Peter	Not.
Ivor	What?
Peter	Blot.
Ivor	Where?
Peter	On your copy-book I'm afraid.
Ivor	Look, for the last time. I'm on my way to a very important business meeting and I seem to have lost my way. Come to think of it, I've lost my car as well. If you've stolen my Jag, it will be the worse for you.
Peter	You're dead!
Ivor	Pardon.
Peter	You're dead.
Ivor	Don't be ridiculous. I'm here talking to you.
Peter	I'm Peter.
Ivor	I rather gathered that, given the sign. *(He points to sign)*
Peter	No, I'm Peter, you know, *the* Peter.

Ivor	Look, I'm sure you're very well known around here, wherever here is, but I'm not from round here.
Peter	No, *the* Peter, keeper of the keys to heaven. You're dead and now you've come to see if I'm going to let you in.
Ivor	If I'm dead, how come I'm standing here, alive and talking to you? No, don't tell me, you're dead too. *(He laughs)*
Peter	Precisely.
Ivor	Look, pal, I don't know what you're on, but it must be pretty strong stuff. Try to get a grasp on reality. The only one round here who is dead is you, and that's dead stoned. You'll be singing 'Mr Tambourine Man' and talking about peace and love in a minute.
Peter	We favour harps rather than tambourines round here, but you're right, peace and love are very high on our agenda.
Ivor	This is ridiculous! I'm off. *(He tries to move but he can't)*
Peter	Sorry, there is no way back and I'm afraid you can't move until we've decided which direction you're headed in.
Ivor	You mean I really am dead.
Peter	I'm afraid so. Killed in a car crash, you were. Tut, tut, driving too fast, 80 miles an hour in a 40 zone. Not a very good start, is it? Not for getting into heaven anyway.
Ivor	So, what do I have to do then? How much is it? Who do I pay?
Peter	Money is not going to help you round here. We need to see what the quality of your life has been.
Ivor	Oh, that's all right then. It's been nothing but quality in my life; nothing but the best for Ivor Fortune.

Peter   I don't think you've quite got the hang of things. We need to find something you've done that we can put in the plus column. *(Looks at clipboard)* There is an awful lot in the minus column.

Ivor   Hang on, what about the 300 people I employed. They wouldn't have had any money without me.

Peter   *(Looks at clipboard)* It says here you used to employ 3,000 people. What happened to them?

Ivor   That's not my fault. There was a recession, the pound was too high, the market shrunk and I couldn't compete with cheap foreign imports. I had no choice, we had to down-size, as we call it.

Peter   You mean, put people out of work.

Ivor   That's not the way we choose to describe it.

Peter   I bet it's not. *(Looks at clipboard)* And in that same year you paid yourself a bonus of £1.3 million and acquired a luxury yacht.

Ivor   Ah, well, that was fully deserved, you see. Without me the company would have gone to the wall. Top executives like me don't come cheap. If you pay people peanuts, you get monkeys.

Peter   You must have employed an awful lot of monkeys, then.

Ivor   That's a bit cheap.

Peter   Rather like your workers, then. Is there anything you can think of which might help your cause?

Ivor	Perhaps if I spoke to the top man, you know, the boss, I'm sure we could come to some arrangement. I would make it worth your while.
Peter	Sorry, I've already told you. It doesn't work like that round here.
Ivor	TISSUE!
Peter	Bless you.
Ivor	No, T.I.S.S.U.E. The Institute for Saving Sick and Unwanted Elephants. I used to support it. Well, I gave some money to it once.
Peter	Why was that?
Ivor	I was on this chat show on the telly and this environ-mentalist, do-gooder bloke was accusing me of being a bloated capitalist. Me! Bloated! The cheek of it! I go . . . rather, I went to the gym three times a week. I soon showed him. There and then I wrote out a cheque for £10,000. That soon shut him up, I can tell you.
Peter	Not exactly an act of unbridled altruism . . . Anything else?
Ivor	I can't think of anything. If you take away making money and being successful, it doesn't leave me with a great deal, does it? Are you sure this is fair?
Peter	Yep, that's the way we do things round here.
Ivor	It seems a strange carry on to me. No wonder the Church is struggling on earth if this is how they run head office. How about I reorganise things for you? You know, bring in some sharp business practices, do a bit of streamlining, increase efficiency, cut costs, improve production, get rid of the dead wood?

Peter	Thank you, but no thank you, we like things as they are.
Ivor	You won't last long like that. Progress, that's the key. Without progress you'll be out of business before you can say 'computerisation'.
Peter	We've been here since before time began and now time no longer exists. Our way is the way that lasts eternally. If your way was so good, how come it's now all over and no more?
Ivor	OK, you win. Point me in the direction of hell. Maybe they'll understand the value of money a bit more.
Peter	No can do old friend. Just between you and me, and don't breathe a word to another living soul – oh, you can't, they're all dead – the Mighty One doesn't believe in hell.
Ivor	Doesn't believe in hell! What kind of a God is that? He needs serious help with his business plan.
Peter	He's the kind of God who is purest love. What kind of a loving God would he be if he created someone out of love and then condemned them to eternal torture? How could he bear to look upon that sight?
Ivor	So what happens to me, then?
Peter	*(Takes broom)* Everyone is welcome in heaven. It's just that some have to start at the very bottom. *(Hands him broom)* Here, take this, the Cherubim's rest room needs a good clean. They are mucky little devils those Cherubim, if you'll pardon the expression.
Ivor	Me, sweeping up! I thought you said there wasn't any hell.
Peter	There isn't, only the one you create for yourself. At least in this hell you have the opportunity to turn it into

heaven. Just think, this is your opportunity to take a new broom and to sweep the slate clean.

Ivor   I suppose so. Are the Cherubim good tippers?

Peter   Come on, you'll learn, in time. Well, actually, out of time. Come on.

Exit Peter and Ivor.

Jonah

This is a very simple sketch to stage because it has only four characters and requires no special scenery. The plant that grows to shield Jonah could easily be just a large leaf above his head. This could be a real leaf or one painted on card.

The point of the story of Jonah is to show that God is a universal God whose goodness, love and mercy are not restricted to a particular nation or group. It also shows the responsibility of those who have discovered God's salvation for them, not to cling to it for themselves, but to share it with others, especially those they consider to be unworthy.

One of my favourite sayings is, 'Don't tell me what you are saved from; tell me what you are saved for.' This, it seems to me, is the lesson Jonah needed to learn and is the lesson we need continually to be reminded of. Hopefully, this sketch is one such reminder.

Enter Jonah (he sits centre stage).

Jonah *(Rubs his head)* Hello, I'm Jonah. You might have heard of me. Apparently I've become quite famous. Still, as one of God's chosen, I suppose it's only to be expected. Cor, it's a hot one today, and no mistake. I wish I'd grabbed my hat when the fish spewed me out. The hat's not going to keep the sun off my head stuck inside that fish, is it? Story of my life that. I might be one of God's chosen, but I'm no luckier now than I ever was.

Enter Captain Ahab.

Ahab You made it then.

Jonah Made what, Ahab?

Ahab After the storm. After we threw you overboard. I see you didn't drown.

Jonah	Very observant! No, the Lord saved me. I was swallowed by a big fish. After three days it spit me out onto dry land. It was God's way of getting me to go to Nineveh.
Ahab	Once we had thrown you overboard everything calmed down and we managed to continue our journey with no problems. We've all started to worship your God now. After all, he is the most powerful.
Jonah	But you can't do that! You're . . . um . . . you know . . .
Ahab	Inferior?
Jonah	Well . . . not exactly . . . more . . . um . . .
Ahab	Unclean?
Jonah	I wouldn't quite put it like that. I've nothing against you personally, you understand, it's just that you're a . . . well . . . How can I put it? You're . . .
Ahab	Gentile?
Jonah	Precisely! Couldn't have put it better myself. After all, he is the God of the Hebrews. We're his specially chosen people and only we can be saved by him.
Ahab	He did save us from the storm. Maybe he has a soft spot for Gentiles as well.
Jonah	Don't be ridiculous! What's the point of being a chosen people if God goes round caring for everybody? Take my word for it; salvation belongs to the Jews alone.
Ahab	Are you sure? It seems to me your God is a bit more generous than you give him credit for.

Jonah	Of course I'm sure! Who is the prophet around here? You stick to sailing ships and leave the theology to me.
Ahab	Well I'm off to pray to him anyway. See you around.

Exit Ahab.

Jonah	Isn't that the trouble with the world today? Everyone is a flipping expert. Do I tell him how to sail ships? No! But there he is, and a Gentile no less, telling me about the God of the Hebrews. He gets saved once from a storm and suddenly he thinks he's a prophet.

Enter Citizen.

Citizen	That was one hell of a bit of preaching you did down there, if you'll pardon the expression.
Jonah	I was only telling it the way it is, Citizen. Forty days more, no, sorry, thirty-nine, one has already gone. Thirty-nine more days and Nineveh will be no more. Completely destroyed it will be, and all it's evil ways. Like I said, the Almighty God has spoken!
Citizen	But everyone has believed you, even the king. They're all fasting and repenting and praying to your God. We reckon he will take pity on us and change his mind about destroying us.
Jonah	Rubbish! Why would our God want to save a bunch of . . . of . . .
Citizen	Gentiles?
Jonah	I was thinking more of immoral, unfit, unbelieving heathens, but Gentiles will do. What would he want to save them for?

Citizen   You never know, and it's well worth giving it a go, don't you think? Anyway, I must go; we're having a big service to ask God to take pity on us. Thanks for your message, by the way, most useful, most useful indeed!

Jonah   They're wasting their time. Why would God go to all that trouble to get me to go to Nineveh and proclaim its destruction, if he wasn't going to see it through? I'll just sit here and see what happens. They've got a shock coming, and no mistake.

(Jonah sleeps)

Enter God.

God   Poor Jonah! He still has so much to learn about me, and what I want from my people. I am not a God of vengeance, but of mercy. I'll make this plant grow over him to shield him from the sun.

Exit God.

(Jonah wakes)

Jonah   Look at that! You see how God looks after his own! He's sent me some shade so I can watch in comfort as Nineveh is being destroyed.

After a while . . .

Jonah   Not much happening! I can see all those fools are still praying. Fat lot of good that will do them. *(He stretches)* All this watching is very tiring. I'll just have a quick nap.

(Jonah sleeps)

Enter God.

God   It's time Jonah learned another lesson, I think. Let's take away the plant and see what he thinks.

Exit God.

(Jonah wakes)

Jonah   Great! Fantastic! Here today and gone tomorrow! What kind of gift is that, I'd like to know. How can God make a plant grow over me and then destroy it after only one day? Not only is it unfair to me, it's unfair to the poor old plant as well!

Enter God.

God   Are you angry about the plant, Jonah?

Jonah   You bet I am! Here I am, doing your work, waiting to see you destroy the city, and now getting baked for my troubles. Come on God, it's hardly fair is it? Couldn't you just destroy them now and get it over with? And then could I go home?

God   I'm not going to destroy them, Jonah. Now they have repented and turned to me, I forgive them. They're free to live in peace.

Jonah   What! I get sea-sick on the ship, was thrown overboard, swallowed by a fish, spewed up on dry land, risked life and limb in Nineveh to get your message across, and now you say, 'I've changed my mind'? What sort of a God are you?

God   A kind and merciful God. One who cares for those he has made.

Jonah   But God, they're . . . well . . . you know . . . um . . . Unclean! Heathens! Immoral! Gentiles! You can't have any truck with them! You're our God! We're your chosen people!

God	Jonah, I made all people, and everything that is on the earth and I love all that I have made! Were you angry and sad because the plant withered and died?
Jonah	Too right, I was! What a waste to destroy something of use to me.
God	My point entirely! Are not all those people and everything in that city of more value than a plant?
Jonah	Not to me they're not!
God	No, Jonah, but to me they are, and isn't that what is important?
Jonah	I guess so, you being God and all, but it seems a funny way for the God of the Hebrews to carry on.
God	But that's the whole point, Jonah. I am not just the God of the Hebrews, or of any nation, or of any sect or denomination. I am the God of the whole of creation, black, white, Jew, Gentile, man, woman, rich or poor. Come on; let's find some more people for you to take the message to.
Jonah	I suppose so, but can I have a rest first? I need to get my head round this. It's all so different from what I've been taught before.
God	Of course you can rest. But then you have to take this message to others, and everywhere your story is told religious people will come to understand that I can never be just their God. I will always be the God of everyone.
Jonah	Wow!

Exit God and Jonah.

The Lottery

The Old Testament passage used at the end of this sketch is Isaiah 55: 1-6. In this passage, God, through the prophet, calls the people back to a better life. A life where they rely much more on God to provide for them while they concentrate on living according to his ways. This is a theme taken up by Jesus himself, not least in his appeal to us to set his kingdom and righteousness above all worldly considerations, rather than the other way round. And he urges this upon us, not so that we can learn to go without worldly things, but so that God can provide them all for us.

The greatest hope of a fulfilled life in our society today seems to be the big finger of the National Lottery. Millions of people play it every week, each hoping they will become a millionaire and so find happiness. Most of us know it is very unlikely to be us this week, but we go on doing it anyway.

The point of the sketch is not to denigrate the Lottery, or to demonise gambling, but to show that there is a much more certain way of finding fulfilment, and a way that is freely open to all.

On stage are two chairs and a table.

Enter Narrator.

Narrator   And so verily it came to pass that the Government begat a green paper, which in turn begat a white paper, which itself begat an Act of Parliament, which begat Camelot, which, in 1994, begat the National Lottery. And the National Lottery begat several millionaires and supported many good causes. And the Politicians and the Directors of Camelot saw that it was very good, and very lucrative; and so they begat scratch cards, which begat a midweek draw, which begat the Thunderball draw. And behold, the people spent billions of pounds attempting to get to the Promised Land, for, as they were assured by the big finger each week, 'It could be YOU!'

Exit Narrator.

Enter Dream and Scheme (Dream carries a bag. Scheme carries a book).

Dream   *(To audience)* Hello! I'm Dream, and one day I'm going to be a millionaire. This week it could be ME!

Dream goes and sits at table.

Scheme   Hello! I'm Scheme, and I want to think about that one.

Dream   *(Takes out pen and pad from his bag)* When is your birthday?

Scheme   *(Reads his book)* What?

Dream   When's your birthday?

Scheme   The 13th of June.

Dream   That's no good. Thirteen is very unlucky.

Scheme   Why don't you add the one and the three together and use four?

Dream   I couldn't do that!

Scheme   Why ever not?

Dream   Four was the number of the house we lived in when I failed my driving test. Six is a good number though, I think I'll use that one.

Scheme   I shouldn't, if I was you.

Dream   Why ever not?

Scheme	Think about it. Six is half of twelve, and twelve is one short of thirteen. Half of thirteen is six and a half which, if you double it, is one more than twelve, which is twice the number you first thought of.
Dream	You're right! Phew! That was close! I nearly used the wrong number.
Scheme	Do you seriously think you will ever win?
Dream	Of course I will. *(Reaches in bag and takes out rabbit's paw)* I've got my lucky rabbit's paw.
Scheme	It wasn't very lucky for the rabbit.
Dream	*(Reaches in bag again)* And my four-leaf clover.
Scheme	But that one has only got three leaves.
Dream	I know, but the man who sold it to me explained that it is truly a four-leaf clover, but one of the leaves fell off.
Scheme	*(Shakes his head)* Oh, that's all right then. Do you really believe all this superstitious nonsense can help you win?
Dream	Superstitious! What do you mean, superstitious? I'm not superstitious at all. Now, to pick my numbers. Here goes, I'm not wearing anything green so, fingers crossed, touch wood, this could well be my week. Even my stars said I would come into money.
Scheme	Come on, I'll walk to the shops with you, so I can watch you throw your money away.
Dream	You won't be saying that next week when I'm a millionaire.

Exit Dream and Scheme.

Enter Narrator.

Narrator   And so it came to pass that on the seventh day the Advertising and Publicity Moguls rested from their great work of selling the Lottery and one of the brightest stars in the firmament presided over the draw.

Exit Narrator.

Enter Dream and Scheme.

Scheme   *(Reads book and then looks up)* Did you win, then? Was it 'YOU'?

Dream   Nearly.

Scheme   How many numbers did you get?

Dream   Two.

Scheme   Two! Not very nearly at all then?

Dream   Never mind, next week could just be my week.

Scheme   That's what you said last week, and the week before, and the week before that.

Dream   OK! OK! Don't go on! Nobody likes a clever dick, and that's for sure.

Scheme   It's your money. You throw it away if you want to. *(He returns to reading his book)*

Dream   What are you reading, anyway?

Scheme   It's the Bible, the book of Isaiah, actually you might like to hear this bit.

Dream   Go on then.

Scheme   'Ho, everyone who thirsts, come to the waters; and you that have no money, come, buy and eat! Come, buy wine and milk without money and without price. Why do you spend your money for that which is not bread, and your labour for that which does not satisfy? Listen carefully to me, and eat what is good, and delight yourselves in rich food. Incline your ear, and come to me; listen, so that you may live.' (Isaiah 55:1-3a)

Dream   Sounds good, that. Is there much like that in the Bible?

Scheme   Lots, you ought to read it sometime.

Dream   I think I will; maybe it will help me pick my numbers for next week.

Scheme   Here, take mine. *(Hands him Bible)* I think you need it.

Dream   Have you ever had a go on the Lottery?

Scheme   No, but I have made money out of it.

Dream   How did you do that?

Scheme   I've got shares in Camelot. Come on, let's go.

Exit Dream and Scheme.

Enter Narrator.

Narrator   'Seek the Lord while he may be found, call upon him while he is near' (Isaiah 55:6). Why not give God a try? Ask him to enter your life. Who knows, this time it could well be YOU, and it is certainly no lottery.

Exit Narrator.

The magistrates

This sketch is very loosely based on John 8:1-11; the account of the woman caught in the very act of adultery. It could be used on Ash Wednesday or any other suitable occasion. This passage calls into question the judgements we make of one another and also our perception of the way in which God judges others and us.

In Britain we pride ourselves on our system of justice; whilst it is a very good system, especially when compared to some parts of the world, it can never be infallible since it is designed and operated by fallible human beings.

There are many who would argue that justice is easier to obtain if you have the necessary wealth than if you are poor and lacking resources. Whether or not this is always true, it is a widely held suspicion.

This sketch takes up that theme, and seeks to highlight the fact that all our judgements are partial and flawed; and that those judgements we make with the most certainty may well be those which are most partial and flawed. This is a truth according to the Scriptures that we cannot remind ourselves of too often.

Three seats are in the centre, if possible raised up. At one side there needs to be a place for the accused to stand and at the other side a seat for the solicitor. There are three magistrates, one being the Chairperson. Tommy is dressed shabbily and has earrings, tattoos, etc. Miles is very smart in a suit and with well-groomed hair.

Enter the three magistrates: the Chair, Mag 1 and Mag 2 (they sit).

Enter Ms Law, the solicitor (she sits).

Chair   Bring in the accused.

Enter policeman with Tommy (Tommy stands in the dock with the policeman at his side).

Chair	State your full name, address and occupation.
Tommy	Tommy Leaf, no fixed abode, constabulary surveillance operative.
Chair	*(Writes notes)* T. Leaf, no address. *(Looks up)* And what on earth is a constabulary surveillance operative, may I ask?
Tommy	I keep a lookout for the police, your worship.
Chair	Mr Leaf, I can assure you this is no laughing matter. You are here on a very serious charge . . . to wit . . .
Tommy	To-whoo!
Chair	Mr Leaf, one more wisecrack out of you and I shall add a charge of contempt of court. Do you understand?
Tommy	Yes, Your Worship. Sorry, Your Worship.
Chair	How do you plead? Guilty or not guilty?
Tommy	Oh, I definitely done it.
Chair	Guilty.
Ms Law	*(Stands up)* If it please Your Worship, I appear on behalf of the defendant.
Chair	Ah, Miss Law, how nice to see you again.
Ms Law	It's Ms!
Chair	Pardon?
Ms Law	It's Ms! *Ms* Law, not Miss.

Chair	Oh, I do beg your pardon. We didn't have Ms's when I was young. Do you have anything to say on behalf of your client before we pass sentence?
Ms Law	Yes, Your Worship. This is my client's first offence.
Mag 1	*(To Chair)* First one he's been caught for, I shouldn't wonder.
Ms Law	As I was saying, this is his first offence. My client has not had an easy life.
Tommy	You can say that again.
Ms Law	He comes from a broken home.
Tommy	It wasn't broken until my dad came back drunk the other night. You should have seen it, there was furniture flying all over the place . . .
Chair	Mr Leaf! If there are any more outbursts from you I shall have you removed from the court.
Tommy	Sorry, Your Worship.
Chair	Miss . . . er . . . Ms Law.
Ms Law	Thank you, Your Worship. As I was saying, life has not been easy for my client and he has not had the best of role models. His father, his two elder brothers, and three of his uncles have all served prison sentences.
Mag 2	*(To Chair)* Not much chance of that lot turning over a new leaf, is there? *(They chuckle)*
Ms Law	I should also like to point out that my client was not involved in the break-in. He was simply the lookout and, unfortunately for him, having warned the others he was the only one to be apprehended. My client is only 19 and,

given it is a first offence, and he played only a minor part in the proceedings, I ask the court for leniency and humbly suggest a non-custodial sentence might be more appropriate here.

Chair   Thank you Miss . . . er . . . Ms Law. We will now consider our verdict and the appropriate sentence.

The magistrates huddle together to discuss their verdict.

Chair   Mr Leaf, having considered the very serious nature of this crime in which you broke into a repository containing large quantities of intoxicating beverages and combustible weeds . . .

Tommy   Hang on a minute! I never done that! I'm not holding my hands up to that! It were a booze and fag warehouse we knocked over!

Chair   . . . and having taken into account the mitigating circumstances so ably set out by your counsel, it is the decision of this court that, in order to protect society from such people as yourself who have no respect for persons or property, you shall serve a prison term of six months. Take him down.

Exit Tommy and the policeman.

Chair   Next case!

Enter Miles and the policeman. (Miles stands in the dock with the policeman at his side.)

Chair   State your full name, address and occupation.

Miles   Miles Better, Superior Mansions, Upper Crustley, company director.

Chair	Mr Better . . .
Mag 1	*(Whispers in Chair's ear)*
Chair	My colleague would like to know if you are related to Mr Jonathan Better, the owner of 'Better Beers and Wines'?
Miles	He is my father, Your Worship, and I am, myself, a director of that company.
Chair	Ah, I see. Now, Mr Better, you are charged with assault and causing grievous bodily harm, to wit, that on the fourteenth day of June you were involved in a disturbance at the Pheasant and Poacher Hostelry on Altercation Street which resulted in serious injury being caused to one Mr Holly Leaf. How do you plead?
Miles	Guilty, Your Worship. And may I say how very much I regret this inexcusable episode in which I acted in a totally and utterly reprehensible manner. I am particularly sorry for the pain I have caused to the victim and for the shame I have brought upon my family and myself.
Chair	Quite! Quite!
Ms Law	*(Stands up)* If it please Your Worship, I appear on behalf of the defendant.
Chair	Thank you Miss . . . er . . . Ms Law.
Ms Law	In mitigation, Your Worship, I should like to say that this is my client's first offence. He comes from a very fine family and has a very good reputation within the business community of this town. The philanthropic activities of my client's family are very well known and he himself is actively involved with a number of local charities. Both my client and Mr Leaf had been drinking that day and the altercation arose over whether or not the cigarettes Mr

Leaf was illegally selling in the public house were from a raid on one of my client's warehouses. My client now accepts this was not so and, in any case, that it would be wrong to try to take the law into his own hands. He is full of remorse for his actions and has voluntarily paid all Mr Leaf's medical expenses. I ask the court to be lenient in this case.

Chair   Thank you Ms Law. I do not think this need detain us for long.

The magistrates huddle together to discuss their verdict.

Chair   Mr Better, the court wishes to stress the very serious nature of this offence. We view the wounding of one human being by another as the gravest of crimes. In all normal circumstances this crime would probably carry a custodial sentence. However, given your obvious remorse concerning your actions, your fine family background, your previous exemplary character, and the probability that you were provoked into this attack, we fine you £100 and warn you as to your future behaviour. If, as seems highly unlikely, you should appear before this court again, you would not receive such clemency.

Miles   Thank you, Your Worship. I am most grateful and I can only apologise once again for my disgraceful behaviour.

Chair   You are free to go.

Exit Miles.

Chair   Good! That's the last case. I don't think I could stand any-more people appearing before us like that odious little criminal, Tommy Leaf.

Mag 2   Absolutely! You can spot his sort as soon as they come into the dock.

Mag 1	He'll never amount to anything. He'll be back. His sort always do.
Chair	True! True! How refreshing to have someone decent in court for a change.
Mag 1	His father is a member of my golf club. Such a nice man.
Mag 2	You could tell Miles was one of us as soon as he came into court.
Chair	He probably did us all a favour anyway. With one of the Leaf family out of action, it was one less to go thieving.
Policeman	Let him who is without sin cast the first stone.
Chair	I beg your pardon, Constable.
Ms Law	He said, 'Let's put the paperwork in and we can all go home.'
Chair	A good idea. I'm ready for a swift gin and tonic before dinner. Anyone care to join me . . . at the golf club?
Mag 1	That sounds good to me.
Mag 2	Me too.
	Exit All.

Palm Sunday

The story of Palm Sunday and the triumphant entry of Jesus into Jerusalem is very well known to us. It's a story that is full of joy and hope as the crowds welcome Jesus.

However, it's another of those occasions when I find myself wondering what the people on the edge of events must have thought. Today, if the average churchgoer saw a load of people tearing down branches from the trees in the park, he or she would be much more likely to brand them as hooligans and vandals, than to join them in welcoming the latest prophet. Similarly, those of us who are parents would be singularly unimpressed by our offspring if the excuse for ruining their new coat was that they used it to carpet the road so the prophet's donkey could walk on it. And yet we hear these things every Palm Sunday and sit in silent approval.

This sketch takes a light-hearted look at these events and puts a slightly different slant on them.

One of the following passages should be read, immediately before the sketch takes place: Matthew 21:1-11, or Mark 11:1-10, or Luke 19:28-40.

Enter Rachel and Salome (they can stand or be seated).

Rachel   He's gone and done it this time, Salome.

Salome   Gone and done what, Rachel?

Rachel   It! It! He's gone and done it!

Salome   I think I've got that much. What I mean is, what is 'it'?

Rachel   He's only gone and got himself arrested, that's all.

Salome   Arrested for what?

Rachel	Wilful and criminal damage; that's what!

Rachel   Wilful and criminal damage; that's what!

Salome   Wilful and criminal damage? That doesn't sound too serious to me. I thought he must have murdered someone.

Rachel   Murdered! I'll murder him when I get hold of him, if they ever let him out. You should have seen the state of his coat when he got home. It looked like some great donkey had walked all over it, and it was his best one.

Salome   Has he got two coats then?

Rachel   No, that's why it was his best one.

Salome   What was this wilful and criminal damage?

Rachel   He only vandalised the municipal palm trees. You know, them nice ones on Mount of Olives Boulevard.

Salome   That doesn't sound too serious. Surely he'll get off with a fine?

Rachel   Not with his record, and not with the company he keeps. He's already been accused of blasphemy, no less. He only got off because that Jesus character bamboozled the Pharisees. But how long can he keep that up? They're a right clever lot them Pharisees, you know.

Salome   Oh, I know, dear. Do you know, one of them told me, well, actually, told my Zech – they don't talk to women, you know – anyway, he told my Zech he had worked out you could get thirteen million, seven hundred and fifty nine thousand, one hundred and forty six and a half cherubim on a half shekel.

Rachel   What would you want to do that for?

Salome   Search me, dear, but it shows how clever them Pharisees are. So what do you think will happen to your lad?

Rachel   I think they'll send him to one of those new tough sandal camps they're setting up.

Salome   They're very tough those, so I've heard.

Rachel   It might do him good though. I mean, throwing your best coat on the floor for a donkey to tread on, cutting down perfectly good palm branches and yelling 'Hosanna! Hosanna!' all over the place. Like a bunch of Nazareth United supporters after they've lost.

Salome   Cheer up, Rachel, it might not be as bad as you think.

Rachel   It's ever since he started hanging around with that Jesus character. Before that you at least knew where you were. He was always a bad lad, but he was a decent bad lad. Now he's got no respect for authority and says stupid things about forgiving people, loving them and stuff like that. I mean, where would we be if we all went round forgiving people and loving them? It would be the end of the world as we know it.

Salome   I know what you mean, dear. But you mark my words, that Jesus will come to a bad end and no mistake. He's one of those 'here today and gone tomorrow' characters. In a few weeks' time he'll be yesterday's news.

Rachel   I hope you're right, dear. I just hope my poor Reuben has got him out of his system by the time he gets out. After all, we don't want all this resurrecting in the future, do we?

Salome   No fear of that, dear. I think it's safe to say we've heard the last of that Jesus character.

Rachel   I do hope so.

Salome   Come on, let's go and see what the courts have to say. You never know, Caiaphas might be having one of his lenient days.

Rachel   I doubt it, but you never know.

Exit Rachel and Salome.

The wedding

This sketch is based on the wedding in Cana. Instead of looking at things from the point of view of Jesus and the Gospel, it highlights the possible thoughts of the principal characters at the wedding. John's Gospel is, quite rightly, interested in the way in which this incident points towards who Jesus is and the kingdom he is ushering in. But I like to think about the other people, what their reactions might have been, and especially that of the bride's mother.

I don't suppose that brides' mothers have changed much over the centuries in their single-minded determination to make sure their daughter's wedding day is the best one ever, and certainly better than that of Mrs So and So's daughter down the road. In the sketch, because the bride's mother is a stereotypical bride's mother, it also allows her to quite innocently come out with the truth at the end. She is unaware of what she is saying, but others around her understand its significance. Isn't this often the way we discover things from one another?

The sketch can either be staged in modern times with modern costume, or in its historical setting at the time of Jesus. The words in italics are used as alternatives when the sketch is staged in its historical setting.

SCENE 1   *No scenery is required. Costumes are either modern dress or traditional costume.*

                     Enter Groom and Best Man (they talk as they walk across from one side to the other).

Groom   (*Agitated*) Are you sure you've sorted everything out? The suits, the cars, the photographer, the reception, the wine . . . and anything else?

Groom   (*Agitated*) *Are you sure you've sorted everything out? The clothes, the carriages, the illustrator, the reception, the wine . . . and anything else?*

Best Man   The church?

Best Man   *The Synagogue?*

Groom   Oh yes, that's right, the church. I knew there was something else. Is it all sorted? Is everything arranged? You know what her mother is like. It will all be my fault if anything goes wrong.

Groom   *Oh yes, that's right, the Synagogue. I knew there was something else. Is it all sorted? Is everything arranged? You know what her mother is like. It will all be my fault if anything goes wrong.*

Best Man   Calm down! Stop panicking! Everything is taken care of. You can rely on me; I'm the *best* best man you could have.

Groom   I don't know about that. It was you who arranged the stag night.

Best Man   How was I to know the taxi driver thought I said take us to the tap-dancing instead of the lap-dancing?

Best Man   *How was I to know the camel driver thought I said take us to the tap-dancing instead of the lap-dancing?*

Groom   Come on, hurry up, I need a quick pint.

          Exit Groom and Best Man.

SCENE 2   *Enter Bride and Mother of the Bride (They talk as they walk across from one side to the other).*

Mother   It's not too late to change your mind, you know. I don't know what you see in him. And that family of his – common as muck, if you ask me.

Bride	Well I didn't ask you. I'm marrying Benjamin tomorrow because I love him and I want to be with him.
Mother	Oh well, it's your funeral.
Bride	Mother!
Mother	Very well, but he will mess something up, you mark my words.
Bride	Come on. I want to check on the flowers.

Exit Bride and Mother.

SCENE 3	*Two tables are placed at the front, one in the centre and the other to one side. Each has a bottle of wine and glasses on it.*
	Enter Jesus, Mary and a couple of friends (they sit at the table to one side, facing audience).
	Enter Bride, Groom, Best Man and Mother – all stand as they enter (they sit at centre table, facing audience).
	All sit.
	Enter waiter/servant who pours wine for centre table. Others help themselves. They all drink (waiter/servant stands to one side).
Mother	I see that free-loading religious nut is here with his friends. Never turns down a free lunch, that one.
Bride	Shut up, Mother!
Best Man	(*Stands up and clears his throat*) Ladies and gentlemen, I give you (*Tries to fill his glass but the bottle is empty*) um . . . er . . . whoops . . .

Mother	Typical! I warned you something like this would happen! It's a disaster, that's what it is, a disaster.
Mary	*(To Jesus)* They've run out of wine, Son.
Jesus	Look, Mother, it's not really got anything to do with me.
Mary	But you could help them, couldn't you, I mean, if you really wanted to . . .
Best Man	I'll ask Jesus, see if he can help.
Mother	Why? Does his dad own an off-licence?
Mother	*Why? Does his dad own a tavern?*
Groom	His dad is a carpenter.
Mother	Oh that's all right then. He could knock you up a wine rack. It's a pity you have nothing to put in it.

(Jesus beckons to waiter/servant and whispers in his ear)

Waiter/servant exits then returns with a water jug. He fills the glasses on the top table.

Best Man	Ladies and Gentlemen, I give you the Bride and Groom.

All stand and toast the Bride and Groom.

Mother	*(Sips wine)* Not bad, not bad at all *(Looks at Jesus)* for a carpenter's son, that is. *(To daughter)* At least when he's around you never have to go hungry or thirsty.
Bride	Mother, that's the first sensible thing you have said all day.

Exit All.

The vineyard rap

Based on Isaiah 5:1-7, this sketch simply tells the story of the parable of the vineyard, but using a modern medium. It would probably be something that might appeal to a youth group to perform. Some of the images used, e.g. the Garden Centre, are, of course, modern images, but the rap still remains faithful to the original parable.

This sketch is especially suitable for any Sunday where the virtues of justice and mercy need to be expounded, or on occasions such as Christian Aid week.

Rapper can be a soloist, or a couple of people could do it together. Chorus can be as many people as are available. This might be especially suitable for a youth group.

Enter Rapper and Chorus. Rapper stands in centre, Chorus behind and to one side.

Rapper Come and gather round people and listen to me,
as I tell you all this story of my vineyard and me,
it was cool, it was great, it was good on the eye,
and I vowed that I would love it till the day that I die.
So I worked and I grafted, and I'm grafting still,
as I laboured in that vineyard on the side of the hill.

Chorus So he worked and he grafted, and he's grafting still,
as he laboured in that vineyard on the side of the hill.

Rapper Now the ground it was good, the best for miles around,
it was rich, and it was fertile and incredibly sound.
So I dug it and I dug it, do you dig what I say?
I was labouring hard, working night and all day.
Clearing boulders and stones, and old beakers and jars,
there were bottles and cans, shoes, and even a vase.

Chorus   He cleared boulders and stones, and old beakers and jars,
he found bottles and cans, shoes, and even a vase.

Rapper   Well I paused just to see all the work I had done,
I was feeling quite pleased with all my toil in the sun,
'I must get me some vines for my vineyard,' I said,
'then I'll plant up my vineyard and make me some bread.'
So I left everything there, and I high-tailed it down
to that new Garden Centre on the edge of the town.

Chorus   So he left everything there, and he high-tailed it down
to that new Garden Centre on the edge of the town.

Rapper   When I got to the Centre, I was ready and game,
just to get the best price for those vines, was my aim.
So I haggled and bartered and I knocked the guy down,
then I left with my vines, high-tailed it back out of town.
And I planted them deep, and I planted them true,
then I watered and tended 'til they grew and they grew.

Chorus   And he planted them deep, and he planted them true,
then he watered and tended 'til they grew and they grew.

Rapper   I constructed a watchtower to guard what I had,
for some of those townsfolk are incredibly bad
and I hewed out a wine vat, to make me some wine,
when the grapes ripened up at the winemaking time.
But imagine my anger when the grapes they were piled,
they were not sweet and juicy; but were acrid and wild.

Chorus   We remember his anger, when those grapes they were piled,
they were not sweet and juicy; but were acrid and wild.

Rapper   Now I want all you people to tell what you see
and judge if you will, 'tween my vineyard and me.
For I gave it great care as I toiled in the sun
so I ask you good people, what more could I have done?

For I gave it such care, as a father a child
but all it gave back were those grapes that were wild!

Chorus   Yes, he gave it great care, as a father a child,
but all he got back were those grapes that were wild!

Rapper   Now the vineyard's no more, it's gone back to the ground,
as I tore out the vines and trampled it down.
There's no pruning or hoeing now; it's all overgrown.
Thick with briers and thorns, no more vines will be grown.
No more rain clouds will rain; no more sunlight will shine,
for that vineyard has come to the end of the line.

Chorus   No more rain clouds will rain; no more sunlight will shine,
for that vineyard has come to the end of the line.

Rapper   But that vineyard is not the only one that I've made
and those vines aren't the only ones to have strayed
from the right way to grow and the right fruit to bear
and they won't be the last, of that I can swear.
So examine yourselves if my vines you would be,
when you grow, as you should, you'll be happy and free.

Chorus   So examine yourselves if his vines you would be,
when you grow, as you should, you'll be happy and free.

Rapper   Justice, mercy and peace are the things I require.
These are much more important than the church or the
    choir,
or the bells, or the service, or the minister too,
it's not just what you say, but the things that you do.
'So just look at my vineyard,' the Lord says today,
'for the vines are my people, so heed what I say!'

Chorus   'So just look at my vineyard,' the Lord says today,
'for the vines are my people, so heed what I say!'

Zacchaeus

One of the things I have always found most appealing about Jesus is that you can always rely on him to say and do the unexpected. He simply did not behave in the way prophets and men of God were supposed to behave. He ate, he drank, he liked a good party, and he associated with all the wrong people. He refused to operate by the accepted conventions of his day, and so the majority dismissed him as a fraud.

In the story of his encounter with Zacchaeus we see all these things rolled into one. This sketch merely retells the story of their meeting and seeks to show what it means to know that all are included in the love of God. Whilst we may dismiss some people as unacceptable, God certainly does not, as Zacchaeus comes to discover.

The Crowd numbers can be as many as desired, but at least eight would be useful.

Zacchaeus is sitting at a table counting money.

Enter Crowd (forming a queue at Zacchaeus' table).

Zacchaeus   Time to pay your taxes! Who wants to be first? Come on, now, don't be shy!

Crowd   *(Mumble and groan)* Oh no! It's Zacchaeus again!

Zacchaeus   *(To first person)* Name?

Reuben   Reuben the Potter.

Zacchaeus   *(Looks down list)* Reuben the Potter . . . 25 shekels.

Reuben   How much?

Zacchaeus Twenty-five shekels! Come on, hurry up, we haven't got all day. There are others waiting, you know.

Reuben pays up, mumbling.

Zacchaeus Next!

Simeon *(Goes to Zacchaeus)* Simeon the Shepherd.

Zacchaeus *(Looks down list)* Thirty shekels.

Simeon Thirty shekels! How come? He only had to pay twenty-five! This is daylight robbery!

Zacchaeus Pay up or it's prison for you. *(Shouting off)* Guard!

Simeon All right! All right! *(Pays money)*

Zacchaeus That's it! I'm off! You will all have to come back tomorrow.

Reuben Where are you going to in such a hurry?

Zacchaeus I've heard this Jesus is coming by today. I want to see what he's like. I'm going to get a good seat at the front.

Simeon Jesus won't want to talk to the likes of you! He's got no time for traitors and sinners!

Crowd *(Shouting)* Yeah, go on, clear off!

Reuben Good religious people like Jesus, and us for that matter, wouldn't be seen dead with the likes of you! You're worse than a common criminal, you are!

Zacchaeus I should be very careful if I were you, taxes can easily go up, you know.

Crowd   *(Shouting)* Clear off, Zacchaeus, you're not wanted around here!

Exit Zacchaeus.

Simeon   Come on everyone, let's go and see Jesus for ourselves.

Exit Crowd.

Enter Zacchaeus.

Zacchaeus   Good, no one is here yet. I'll get a good spot at the front. I need it, being slightly vertically challenged. I'll be able to see well from here.

Enter Crowd.

Simeon   *(To the others)* Look, there's Zacchaeus! What a cheek, thinking he can stand with the rest of us.

Reuben   Come on, let's put him where he belongs.

Joseph   What about the taxes?

Simeon   Don't be such a coward, Joseph! This is a matter of principle. We can't have the likes of him standing with decent people as Jesus goes by.

Reuben   We don't want Jesus thinking the citizens of Jericho have no standards, do we?

The Crowd moves towards Zacchaeus.

Reuben   What are you doing there, Zacchaeus?

Zacchaeus   Waiting for Jesus, of course.

Reuben   Not there, you're not. That spot is for decent folk.

Reuben pushes Zacchaeus behind him. Zacchaeus moves next to Reuben.

Simeon   *(To Zacchaeus)* What are you doing here?

Zacchaeus   I've told you before, waiting for Jesus.

Simeon   That's my place, out of the way!

Simeon pushes Zacchaeus behind him. Zacchaeus moves next to Simeon.

Joseph   *(Pushes Zacchaeus behind him)* My place, I think.

The rest of the Crowd moves Zacchaeus out of the way until they are in two rows and he is behind them unable to see.

Zacchaeus   *(Climbs on chair or steps or pulpit)* I'll just have to watch from this tree. I'll get them back though, you mark my words. I've made a note of all their names. It's double taxes for them.

Enter Jesus.

Reuben   Hello Jesus, welcome to Jericho.

Jesus stops.

Reuben   We're big fans of yours, oh yes. Love your stories! Are you doing any miracles today?

Simeon   It's wonderful to meet a prophet. We're all very religious you know. Synagogue every Saturday, pay our tithes, make our sacrifices. Keep most of the Commandments.

Joseph   All of them!

Simeon	Oh yes, that's right, all of them.
Jesus	*(Looks up)* What are you doing in that tree Zacchaeus?
Zacchaeus	Who, me? Not a lot, just hanging around.
Jesus	Well, hurry up and come down! I'm starving and you're giving me dinner.
Zacchaeus	*(Gets down from tree)* Me! Dinner! Are you sure you've got the right Zacchaeus?
Jesus	Absolutely! Now come over here.
Zacchaeus	*(Pushes his way through the crowd)* Excuse me! Out of the way! Let me through, thank you!

Zacchaeus comes and stands with Jesus.

Jesus	*(Puts his arm round Zacchaeus)* It is all right about dinner, isn't it?
Zacchaeus	What! Yes! You bet!
Reuben	Well! Have you ever seen anything like that? Calls himself a prophet! If he were from God he would never associate with a hopeless lot like Zacchaeus!
Simeon	'You are judged by the company you keep,' my mother used to say.
Joseph	I can't stand here and watch this! I mean, Zacchaeus of all people! What's wrong with us?
Reuben	Nothing! Come on, let's go and listen to the Pharisees. At least they know how to conduct themselves properly, as befits religious people.

Exit Crowd (shouting as they go).

Crowd   Fraud! Charlatan! Impostor!

Zacchaeus   Look, Jesus, there is something I have to do before you come into my house. I've been a bad lot, you see. I've swindled and cheated and robbed people blind.

Jesus   I know.

Zacchaeus   No, don't try and stop me. I have to get it all off my chest . . . You know?

Jesus   Yes.

Zacchaeus   Oh! But I have come to a decision. I'm going to give half my fortune to the poor and anyone I've cheated I'll repay four times over. How does that sound?

Jesus   Very good, Zacchaeus.

Zacchaeus   Apart from that lot, of course. *(Points to Crowd)* They can pay double.

Jesus   Even that lot must be included, Zacchaeus.

Zacchaeus   Are you sure?

Jesus   I'm sure.

Zacchaeus   But they did call you a lot of awful names. Shouldn't they be punished, even just a little bit?

Jesus   No, Zacchaeus, all are included.

Zacchaeus   All?

Jesus   All.

Zacchaeus Very well.

Jesus   Now, where is this dinner?

Zacchaeus This way, Lord; just one question . . .

Jesus   What's that?

Zacchaeus Why choose me? There are many more deserving cases than me, that's for sure.

Jesus   I came to seek out and to save the lost, Zacchaeus, and that certainly includes you.

Zacchaeus What a difference it makes to be included. Let's go and get dinner.

Exit Jesus and Zacchaeus.